This book belongs to

ISBN: 978-1-63578-501-2

Current contact information for Libro Studio LLC can be found at www.LibroStudioLLC.com

Printed in Great Britain
by Amazon

56449978R00059